G000241653

Cover illustration: A Ferret Mk 2/3 armoured car of the 4th Royal Tank Regiment patrols the shore of the Western Aden Protectorate. (*Soldier*)

1. Using the same ammunition as the towed 105mm Light Gun, Abbot carries 40 rounds, six of which are HESH for the anti-tank role and the remainder HE and Smoke. Maximum rate of fire is 12 rounds per minute out to a range of 17,000m. Ammunition is loaded separately, the projectile by means of a power rammer and the cartridge by hand.

TANKS ILLUSTRATED NO. 12

British Army FIGHTING VEHICLES

1945 to the present

SIMON DUNSTAN

ARMS AND ARMOUR PRESS
London—Melbourne—Harrisburg, Pa.—Cape Town

Introduction

Tanks Illustrated 12: British Army Fighting Vehicles, 1945 to the present
Published in 1984 by Arms and Armour Press,
Lionel Leventhal Limited, 2–6 Hampstead High
Street, London NW3 1QQ; 11 Munro Street, Port
Melbourne 3207, Australia; Sanso Centre,
9 Adderley Street, P.O. Box 94, Cape Town 8000,
South Africa; Cameron and Kelker Streets, P.O.
Box 1831, Harrisburg, Pennsylvania 17105, USA

British Library Cataloguing in Publication Data:
Dunstan, Simon
British Army fighting vehicles, 1945 to the present.
(Tanks illustrated; 12)
1. Armoured vehicles, Military – Great Britain –
History – Pictorial works
I. Title   II. Series
623.74'7510941   UG446.5
ISBN 0-85368-669-6

Editing and layout by Roger Chesneau.
Typeset by CCC, printed and bound in Great
Britain by William Clowes Limited,
Beccles and London.

Henry

Although the Main Battle Tank (MBT) remains the principal land weapon system, it could not perform effectively on the battlefield without the support of myriad other armoured fighting vehicles (AFV). The photographs on the following pages depict the family of vehicles currently in service with the British Army; new equipments such as the SP70 (a 155mm self-propelled howitzer) are excluded since procurement plans have not yet been finalised.

After 1945 the British Army favoured wheeled vehicles such as the Ferret and Saladin for the reconnaissance role, primarily for their quietness and ease of maintenance, but with improved technology the function is now fulfilled by the successful and extensive Scorpion CVR(T) range. Similarly, wheeled APCs have given way to the tracked vehicles of the FV430 series, which are also employed for specialised purposes, as are a number of variants based on the chassis of past and present MBTs. Apart from the FV433 Abbot, the current inventory of self-propelled (SP) tube and missile artillery is exclusively of American origin. These SP weapons are also used by several NATO allies, which is advantageous to the concept of standardisation within the armies of Western Europe.

Unless otherwise noted, all the photographs are reproduced by courtesy of the Ministry of Defence Public Relations departments, to whom I extend my thanks, as I do to Paul Haley of *Soldier* magazine for his excellent photographs of the Falklands War.

Simon Dunstan

2. The M107 is one of a family of US vehicles based on a common chassis and produced by the Pacific Car and Foundry Company, the FMC Corporation and Bowen-McLaughlin-York. The 175mm M113 gun has a maximum elevation of 65°, a 2° depression and a traverse of 30° left and right. A large recoil spade is mounted at the rear to absorb the shock when the massive weapon is fired.

3. A Ferret Mk 1/1 Scout Car leads a Chieftain Bridgelayer over a No. 9 Tank Bridge across a stream on the Hohne Ranges in West Germany. Designed to replace the highly successful Daimler Scout Car of the Second World War, the Ferret entered service with the British Army in 1952 and remained in production until 1972, by which time 4,409 vehicles had been manufactured. The Mk 1 has an open-topped compartment for enhanced observation by the commander of the two-man crew and is principally used for liaison duties. The Mk 1 is an up-armoured model fitted with side and rear hull plates of increased thickness during production.

4. The Reconnaissance Platoon of the 10th Prince. Mary's Own Gurkha Rifles, mounted in Ferret Mk 1/2 LRVs (Light Reconnaissance Vehicles), guard the British sovereign base of Dhekelia in Cyprus during the fighting between Turkish and Greek Cypriots following the invasion of the island by Turkish forces on 20 July 1974. The Ferret Mk 1/2 is a basic Mk 1 with a small, flat-faced turret and an externally mounted machine-gun (in this instance an L4A4 7.62mm Bren gun).

◄3

▼4

A Ferret Mk 2/3 Scout Car of the 1st Battalion the Royal Welch Fusiliers is halted on a mountain road in Hong Kong during a reconnaissance patrol. The Mk 2 is the most common model of the Ferret and incorporates a turret mounting an L3A3 (.30 calibre Browning) machine-gun. The original Mk 2 with machine-gun turret had thinner hull plates, whereas the Mk 2/3 was up-armoured during production. The Mk 2/1 was a basic Mk 2 with stowage for a Bren gun; the Mk 2/4 was a Mk 2 up-armoured post-production with appliqué plates; and the Mk 2/5 was an up-armoured Mk 2/1. The Mk 2/2 was a locally modified version used in the Far East with an extension collar between the hull and the turret to give a greater field of fire.

Clad in a protective 'Noddy' suit against nuclear and chemical attack, the commander of a Ferret Mk 2/3 FV701(H) Scout Car of the 2nd Battalion the Royal Irish Rangers conducts his vehicle through a West German town during Exercise 'Swordthrust' in October 1975. Note the numerous fuel jerrycans and various purloined ammunition boxes for extra stowage strapped to the vehicle.

5▶

6▼

Well concealed in the undergrowth, a Ferret Mk 2/3 of the 17th/21st Lancers undertakes a reconnaissance mission in West Germany. Since its inception the Ferret has been the standard reconnaissance and liaison vehicle of the infantry and Royal Armoured Corps and, indeed, virtually every branch of the Army. Unlike the practice in some contemporary armies, British reconnaissance vehicles are not intended to fight in order to gain intelligence but to observe and rely on their high mobility to avoid contact with the enemy.

8. An unarmed Ferret Mk 2/3 Scout Car of the 1st Battalion The Cheshire Regiment serving with the Berlin Brigade conducts a patrol alongside the infamous Berlin Wall. Powered by a Rolls-Royce 1360 Mk 6A engine, the Ferret incorporates four-wheel drive with five forward and five reverse gears, giving excellent cross-country performance.

9. Travelling at speed between white tapes marking a clear lane through a minefield, a Ferret Mk 2/3 Scout Car takes part in a battle-group exercise at Suffield in Canada. The Ferret, like numerous outstanding British weapons systems of the 1950s, has enjoyed considerable export success and has served in the armies of at least 27 nations.

8▲ 9▼

◄7

▲10   ▼11

10. A pair of FV711 Ferret Mk 4 Scout Cars stand guard at an airport in Belize. A logical development of previous models, the Mk 4 had strengthened suspension and larger (11.00 × 20) wheels, hence the nickname 'Big Wheel Ferret'. This allows for the carriage of more or heavier equipment, and gives improved performance over rough terrain. Used only by the British Army, it is equipped with a bellows-type flotation screen which, when erected, allows the vehicle to propel itself across lakes and rivers by means of its wheels. The Mk 3 is a Ferret Mk 1/1 to the same standard as the Mk 4 but with the addition of a machine-gun turret.

11. An FV712 Ferret Mk 5 Scout Car of 'A' Squadron, The Blues and Royals, is prepared for firing on the range at Hjerkin, Norway, during Exercise 'Hardfall', to train members of NATO's ACE (Allied Command Europe) Mobile Force in Arctic warfare and survival. The heaviest of all Ferret models, the Mk 5 has a modified turret with pins for four Swingfire missiles and a machine-gun mounting. The Mk 5 is no longer in service and was intended only as an interim vehicle pending the introduction of the FV438 and FV102 Striker. An earlier model, the FV203 Ferret Mk 2/6, mounted one Vigilant anti-tank guided missile either side of the turret of a Mk 2/3. When the Mk 2/6 was superseded by the Mk 5, the missile system was removed and the vehicle reverted to the reconnaissance role, becoming the Ferret Mk 2/7.

12. Originally designated Combat Vehicle Reconnaissance (Wheeled) and designed as the companion vehicle to the CVR(T) Scorpion, the Fox has been developed from the 'Big Wheel Ferret' but incorporates new technology such as aluminium armour and a 30mm Rarden gun in the turret. The Fox is employed by three British armoured reconnaissance regiments, one Regular and two Territorial Army (TA) – the Royal Yeomanry and the Queen's Own Yeomanry.

13. Besides its powerful main armament, Fox embodies numerous observation and surveillance instruments, including a Rank Precision Industries SPAV L2A1 passive night sight to the right of the 30mm Rarden, which gives a full night-fighting capability. The collapsible flotation screen around the hull of this vehicle is only fitted to export models – the registration letters 'MS' denote foreign Military Sales. The Fox is in service with the armies of Iran, Kenya, Malawi, Nigeria and Saudi Arabia as well as that of the United Kingdom.

14. A Fox armoured car of the 2nd Royal Tank Regiment patrols through the bomb-damaged centre of Castlederg in Northern Ireland. Two squadrons of the Royal Armoured Corps based at Omagh in Ulster employ the Fox in the medium reconnaissance role. The Royal Ordnance Factory (ROF) at Leeds currently offers for export a number of variants based on the Fox, including the Panga, Fox/Milan, Fox/Scout and a version mounting the 25mm Hughes Chain Gun.

12▲

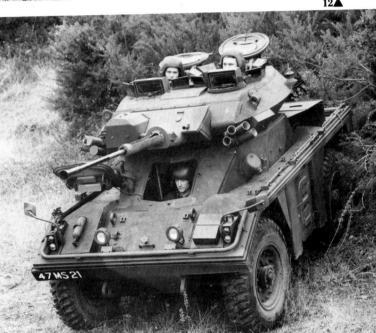

13▲

▲15 ▼16

15. With the collapse of law and order in Northern Ireland, the local company of Short Brothers and Harland Ltd of Belfast produced an armoured patrol vehicle based on the well-proven chassis of the Land Rover; an armoured personnel carrier, the Short SB.301, was subsequently developed as a companion vehicle. Both the FV18061 Shorland Mk 3 (right) and the Short SB.301 (left) are used by the British Army, the Ulster Defence Regiment and the Royal Ulster Constabulary. (Simon Dunstan)

16. Shortly after the Second World War, Alvis Ltd of Coventry, in conjunction with the FVRDE (Fighting Vehicle Research and Development Establishment), undertook the design of a standard chassis as the basis for a family of vehicles known as the FV600 series. The Malayan Emergency accelerated the development of the FV603 APC version, Saracen, and it entered service in 1952. Throughout the 1950s and 1960s, the Saracen was the standard APC of the British Army until it was superseded from 1963 by the FV432 tracked APC. In the background is Saracen's sister vehicle, a Saladin armoured car of the Queen's Own Hussars on patrol in Hong Kong.

17. A Saracen demonstrates its ability to manoeuvre freely with any one wheel missing due to mine damage during a display at Bovington. Powered by a Rolls-Royce B80 Mk 6A engine, Saracen carries eight infantrymen, a commander and a driver at a speed of 45mph to a range of 250 miles. There are several variants of Saracen, including the FV604 Command Vehicle, the FV610(A) Artillery Command Vehicle and the FV611 Ambulance, as well as export models which are in service with a dozen nations. (Simon Dunstan)

18. The Saracen remains in service with the British Army in its specialised roles and as an APC in the Yeomanry; a significant number are employed for internal security duties in Northern Ireland, such as this Black Watch example, at a vehicle checkpoint near the border. The standard armament is a turret-mounted L3A3 machine-gun and a Bren LMG on a ring mounting above the troop compartment.

▲19

20▶

19. A Saladin Armoured Car of the Royal Scots Dragoon Guards manoeuvres across country in the Pentland Hills. After entering British Army service in 1959, Saladin became the standard heavy armoured car of the Royal Armoured Corps in BAOR and overseas, fighting with considerable success in numerous security campaigns from Cyprus to the Far East.

20. Well-camouflaged beneath scrim netting, a Saladin of the Queen's Own Hussars conducts a patrol in Hong Kong. Besides its principal tactical role of reconnaissance, Saladin has often provided close fire support for infantry using its 76.2mm L5A1 gun firing HE, Smoke, Illuminating and Canister rounds; a HESH (High Explosive Squash Head) projectile gives the vehicle a creditable tank-killing capability.

21. A Sioux helicopter overflies a Saladin of the 17th/21st Lancers during an exercise in Cyprus. Secondary armament to the 76.2mm main gun comprises a coaxial L3A3 machine-gun, with a similar weapon mounted to the right of the commander's hatch; six electrically fired smoke dischargers are fitted to either side of the turret. Saladin has been replaced by the FV101 Scorpion in Cavalry reconnaissance regiments, but some are still in use by TA Yeomanry units and with the armoured reconnaissance squadron based in Cyprus. It also remains in service with a score of other countries.

22. Flying a large Union Flag, a Saladin of the 16th/5th The Queen's Royal Lancers acts as an escort to the Nicosia Convoy carrying British dependants during the Turkish invasion of Cyprus in 1974.

◀**21**

22▼

23. An FV101 Scorpion of 'A' Squadron, The Blues and Royals, leads two 'Big Wheel Ferrets' during Exercise 'Alexander Express', held in the mountainous areas of Northern Greece. By designation the Combat Vehicle Reconnaissance (Tracked) or CVR(T) and not a light tank, Scorpion entered service with the British Army in January 1972.

24. A group of Scorpions trundle along a forest track during an exercise in West Germany. In order to meet the stringent weight limitations for 'air-transportability' – two vehicles can be carried in a C-130 Hercules – the hull and turret are fabricated of aluminium armour, giving protection from heavy machine-gun fire (projectiles up to 14.5mm) over the frontal aspect and against 7.62mm armour-piercing rounds over the rest of the vehicle.

25. Speeding through a clearing whilst on exercises in West Germany, a Scorpion of 'C' Squadron, The 17th/21st Lancers, displays its superb mobility. The 190bhp Jaguar J60 (a derated version of the Jaguar XK sports car petrol engine) provides a high power-to-weight ratio, giving a cross-country performance which is only limited by the amount of physical discomfort the crew can withstand. Top speed is officially stated to be 50mph, but speeds in excess of the maximum limit on British roads have been achieved.

23 ▶

▼24

26. One squadron of Scorpions is stationed Belize in Central America, to deter aggression from the neighbouring 'Guats' (Guatemala). Here a Scorpion of 'C' Squadron, the Life Guards, moves throug a jungle village. Scorpion is armed wit a 76mm L23A1 gun (a lighter version of that fitted to Saladin), whic fires a comprehensive range of projectiles, an 40 rounds are carried. The gunner sits in the right-hand side of the turret (the commande is to his left) and controls both the main armament and the L43A1 coaxial machine-gun (which also acts as a ranging weapon).

27. Bedecked with Union Flags on all quarters, a Scorpion of the 16th/5th The Queen's Royal Lancers patrols the perimeter of a Sovereign Base Area (SBA) during the Turkish invasion of Cyprus. During one such patrol, a Scorpion encountered a Turkish M47 tank encroaching on the SBA. With his 76mm gun levelled at point-blank range against the 90mm of the M47, the Scorpion's commander eventually persuaded the Turkish crew of their map-reading error and an unequal tank battle was avoided.

▲26

◀27

18

On 21 May 1982 o troops of 'B' quadron, The Blues d Royals, landed at n Carlos Bay in the lklands in support of e marines and ratroopers of 3 ommando Brigade. os. 3 and 4 Troops ch comprised two orpion and two cimitar vehicles. They ovided invaluable fire pport to the infantry ttalions in the battles r the hills overlooking ort Stanley, notably at ount Longdon and at ireless Ridge. (Paul aley/*Soldier*)

. As a companion to orpion, Scimitar is sically the same hicle except that the rret mounts a 30mm arden gun. Tactically, wever, their tasks fer, the Scorpion ing employed in the edium reconnaissance le and the Scimitar r close reconnaissance. the five armoured connaissance giments of 1 (Br) orps of BAOR, each giment has 32 orpions, 40 Scimitars, Spartans, 7 Sultans, Samsons and 3 maritans – embracing e complete range of VR(T) except Striker.

28▲

29▶

▲30 ▼31

30. Powered by the same Jaguar engine as Scorpion, Scimitar has even greater agility, owing to its lighter weight. The British Army first received Scimitar in March 197. To fulfil its close reconnaissance role, Scimitar is assigned from its parent regiment in independent troops in infantry battle groups.

31. A Scimitar moves through a debris-littered street in Port Stanley soon after the ceasefire. The 30mm Rarden, firing HE and APSE (Armour Piercing Secondary Effect), in conjunction with the image-intensifier night sights, proved particularly effective in the night battles, engaging pin-point targets with the Rarden and enemy positions with sustaine coaxial machine-gun fire at ranges of 800m. (Paul Haley/*Soldier*)

32. In a typical AFV hide, a Scimitar of 'B' Squadron, The 17th/21st Lancers, lies concealed beneath natural vegetation as it waits for enemy forces to advance during Exercise 'Avon Express'. The compact dimensions of CVR(T allow it to manoeuvre through such wooded terrain with ease – one of the original design specifications required that CVR(T) be able t negotiate between the trees of rubber plantations in the Far East.

33. The FV103 Sparta is the APC version in the CVR(T) range. It was first issued in 1976 and entered service in BAOR during 1978. The crew of Spartan comprises driver and commander/machine-gunner, with accommodation for fo troops and their equipment. Spartan is employed in a variety roles, for example as a carrier for Blowpipe teams and combat engineers with their demolition stores and a missile resupply vehicle for Striker. Th Spartan of the 1st Roya Tank Regiment carrie a No. 14 (ZB 298) surveillance radar.

32▲   33▼

▲34 ▼35

34. With the distinctive ACE Mobile Force insignia on its side, a Spartan takes part in an exercise in Norway guarding NATO's northern flank. As with all vehicles in the CVR(T) range, Spartan has excellent flotation, and snow presents no impediment to mobility; similarly, all members are fitted with a wading screen in order to negotiate water obstacles.

35. Festooned with 'camo' nets and impedimenta, a Spartan undergoes a joint NATO exercise in West Germany. There are several variants of Spartan currently under development, either for export or for possible service with the British Army, particularly in the anti-aircraft role. These include a Spartan chassis with a French TA20 twin 20mm cannon turret and one fitted with a multiple Blowpipe launcher. There are also several designs mounting various Anti-Tank Guided Weapon systems including TOW, HOT and Milan.

36. An FV105 Sultan Armoured Command Vehicle of the 1st Royal Tank Regiment partakes in a training exercise in West Germany. Sultan features an enlarged superstructure, in order to accommodate additional crew members, radios, map boards etc. for the command role. Armament comprises a single pintle-mounted L7A2 7.62mm machine-gun. Superseding the FV604 and FV610 Saracen command vehicles, Sultan entered service with the British Army in April 1977.

37. Sultan can be configured to meet the particular needs of various units, but standard equipment includes a detachable 10m pole aerial over the engine covers and an extending 'penthouse' at the rear for increased working area under cover. Here, the aerial and penthouse are being erected on a Sultan parked in a woodland clearing. (Simon Dunstan)

▲38   ▼39

38. The FV104 Samaritan is an armoured ambulance built to the same configuration as Sultan except for the enlarged rear door to facilitate the loading and unloading of casualties. Samaritan has crew of two, a driver and commander/medical orderly. Up to four stretcher cases can be carried and, being an ambulance, the vehicle is unarmed. This view of a Samaritan of the 17th/21st Lancers in Norway illustrates the air-conditioning unit mounted in the rear door and the comprehensive medical supplies carried in stowage lockers on the roof.

39. Based on the same hull as Spartan, the FV102 Striker is an anti-tank guided weapon vehicle equipped with five Swingfire missiles in launcher bins on the roof at the rear. It entered service with BAOR in 1976 and has a crew of three comprising driver, commander and missile operator. Striker is currently operated by anti-tank regiments of the Royal Artillery. (Simon Dunstan)

40. With the characteristic pale blue berets and white livery of the United Nations Peace Keeping Forces, the crew of a Ferret Mk 1/1 check their map before a patrol in Cyprus. (*Soldier*)

41. A Saladin armoured car of the Queen's Own Hussars manoeuvres through the narrow streets of the infamous Crater district in Aden. (*Soldier*)

▲42

42. FV101 Scorpions negotiate a river bed during a reconnaissance mission in the Central American state of Belize. (*Soldier*)

43. The 105mm main armament of an FV433 Abbot is trained on a target during a firepower demonstration at Larkhill. (Simon Dunstan)

44. An M109A1 155mm Self-Propelled Howitzer prepares to fire during a training exercise on Salisbury Plain. (Simon Dunstan)

45. CVR(T) Scorpions traverse a No. 8 Tank Bridge at speed during a mobility demonstration at Bovington. (Simon Dunstan)

▼43

▲46 ▼47

6. A pair of Scorpions
and a Fox armoured car
take part in the finale of
firepower
demonstration at
Lulworth. (Simon
Dunstan)

7. An FV432
Armoured Personnel
Carrier moves forward
during a battle-group
exercise at Suffield in
Canada.

8. A Swingfire missile
leaps from its launcher
bin; a further five
missiles are carried
inside the vehicle and
are loaded by a crew
member from outside.
The Swingfire has a
range of up to 4,000m
and the HEAT warhead
can defeat all main
battle tanks currently in
service.

9. The crew of a
Striker anti-tank guided
weapon vehicle stow the
remote control for the
Swingfire missile
system. This facility
allows the missiles to be
fired from up to 100m
from the vehicle, which
can thus be hidden
behind a crest or under
cover so that the
signature of the missile
launch is obscured from
the enemy. (Simon
Dunstan)

29

▲50 ▼51

30

52▲

50. The armoured recovery vehicle of the CVR(T) range is the FV106 Samson. The hull configuration is similar to that of the Spartan APC, with a winch mounted in the rear and twin earth spades at the back. The vehicle is liberally endowed with tow bars, towing cables and tool boxes on the exterior. (Simon Dunstan)

51. A Samson ARV pulls an FV434 Maintenance Vehicle out of trouble; maximum pull with a 4:1 snatch block arrangement (as illustrated) is 12,000kg. An A-frame jib crane can be fitted at the rear to lift heavy equipment and vehicle assemblies. (Simon Dunstan)

52. The two troops of The Blues and Royals were supported in the Falklands by a Samson ARV which recovered many stranded vehicles, although the Scorpions and Scimitars performed very well in the boggy conditions, covering an average of 350 miles each. One vehicle was badly damaged by a mine but no crew casualties were suffered. Besides the fire support role, the vehicles played an important part in moving supplies and casualties, and in route clearing and reconnaissance. (Paul Haley/*Soldier*)

▲53 ▼54

3. Originally known as Trojan, the FV432 Armoured Personnel Carrier was developed by FVRDE and production was undertaken by GKN Sankey of Shropshire from 1962 until 1971. The first model, the Mk 1 (illustrated here), is powered by a Rolls-Royce B.81 petrol engine and entered service in 1963. The Mk 1 and Mk 1/1 have the silencer and exhaust pipe mounted on the left-hand side of the roof. The first 54 Mk 1s (02EA01–02EA54) did not have the internal floor strengthened for the 81mm mortar role and were redesignated Mk 1/1. The name Trojan was dropped because it infringed a commercial trademark.

4. The FV432 is amphibious by means of a flotation screen mounted around the hull top which can be erected in about two minutes. When afloat, the vehicle is propelled by its tracks. Most FV432s have now had their flotation screens removed; the APC can ford water up to 3½ft deep without preparation. This Mk 1 has its screen and trimvane erected as it prepares for a wading trial. The petrol-engined Mk 1 and 1/1 have been employed only for training purposes in the UK and at BATUS in Canada.

55. A pair of FV432 Mk 2/1 APCs of the 1st Staffords motor across the Achmer training area. The Mk 2 differs from the Mk 1 in that its prominent silencer and exhaust pipe are mounted on the left-hand side of the hull rather than on the roof. An L7A2 GPMG is mounted by the commander's hatch.

56. Painted in the standard sand yellow and green striped camouflage scheme of vehicles at the British Army Training Unit Suffield (BATUS) in Canada, an FV432 Mk 1 thunders across the prairie. One identifying feature of the Mk 1 is the large NBC filter housing on the right-hand side of the hull. This vehicle is fitted with an enclosed Peak Engineering machine-gun turret.

▲57

57. Soldiers of the 1st Battalion The Prince of Wales's Own Regiment of Yorkshire, disembark from their 432s during an exercise in West Germany. The machine-guns of the APCs can provide limited fire support to infantry in the assault.

58. An FV432 Mk 2 named 'Poelcappelle' – after the Flanders village that was the scene of savage fighting during the Third Battle of Ypres – moves at speed on exercise at Sennelager in West Germany. The first 280 Mk 2s (08EA01–10EA80) feature the same prominent NBC air ventilation housing in the right-hand hull side as that in the Mk 1 and Mk 1/1 vehicles.

59. Infantry climb aboard their FV432 Mk 1 at BATUS in Canada. The APC transports a crew of two and up to ten infantrymen. Weighing 14 tons, the all-welded steel hull provides protection against small-arms fire and shell splinters.

◀**59**

60. The FV432 is the most numerous AFV in service with the British Army, and the basic chassis has been converted to a variety of roles; those shown here include (from left to right) the FV432 Rarden, FV432 81mm Mortar, APC FV432 Mk 2, FV434 Carrier Maintenance Vehicle and FV432 Wombat.

61. The replacement for the FV432 is the MCV 80, which is scheduled to enter service in the late 1980s. The British Army has a requirement for 1,000 vehicles with a range of variants including command, recovery, mortar, combat engineer and repair vehicles. An initial batch of 250 vehicles is being built by GKN Sankey, each powered by a Rolls-Royce Condor 8V800 diesel engine coupled to a Detroit-Diesel Allison X-300-4B transmission, giving enhanced mobility and the capability to keep pace with the Challenger MBT over all manner of terrain. The squad vehicle is armed with a Rarden 30mm Cannon and a Hughes Helicopters 7.62mm M230 Chain Gun, mounted coaxially. (Simon Dunstan)

▲62

▲63

62. A wounded soldier of the 1st Battalion The Prince of Wales's Own Regiment of Yorkshire, is swiftly evacuate in an FV432 Ambulance during an exercise in West Germany. The vehicle carries four stretcher cases or two stretcher cases and five seated casualties in addition to its two-man crew.

63. An FV432 Mk 2/1 with a 120mm Wombat L6 recoilless rifle reverses into a hide on the edge of a wood whilst on exercise in West Germany. The vehicle is served by a crew of five comprising driver, commander, gunner and two loaders to handle the bulky 120mm ammunition of which only 14 rounds are carried. The 120mm Wombat has now been replaced by the Milan anti-tank guided missile system which is deployed by its crew away from the vehicle.

64. A soldier of the King's Own Royal Border Regiment sights the 120mm Wombat mounted on an FV432 Mk 2/1; above the weapon is a .50 calibre spotting rifle to establish the range to target. The Wombat can be fired from its position above the roof or unloaded by means of a winch and ramps for operation on a ground mounting. Other 432s in the anti-armour role feature an 84mm Carl Gustav rocket launcher mounted on a simple bar rest fitted across the roof hatch.

65. The 81mm Mortar L16A1 is fired through the main roof hatch of an FV432 Mk 2/1 Mortar Carrier. Each mechanised infantry battalion has six mortar carriers in its support company. The 81mm mortar can be traversed through 360° and up to 160 bombs, both HE and Smoke, are carried internally. The vehicle has a six-man crew. Note the smaller housing of the NBC ventilation system on the vehicle side – the principal identifying feature of the Mk 2/1.

66. When fitted with map boards, folding tables and additional communications equipment, the FV432 is employed as a command vehicle. A portable generator to power the extra radios and lighting is mounted above the engine compartment, and to create additional working space a penthouse can be erected along the side of the hull – seen here rolled up in the stowed position on this Mk 1. The command vehicle carries five staff members besides the two-man crew.

◄64

67. In addition to the command vehicle, there are several versions of the 432 in service with the Royal Artillery fitted with specialized equipment such as the EMI Cymbeline mortar-locating radar, the Marconi Space and Defence Systems Field Artillery Computer Equipment (FACE, for the battery command role) and the Plessey Sound ranging system (Sound Ranging Radio Link No. 2 Mk 1, for controlling counter-battery fire). Here, a FV432 crosses the 'double bridging' of a Centurion single-span No. 6 Tank Bridge and a Chieftain No. 8 bridge. This technique allows the total bridging distance to be greatly increased so as to span especially wide obstacles.

68. A special version of the FV432 used by the Royal Corps of Signals is the FV439 which acts as a mobile radio relay station. Here an FV439 attached to the 1st Battalion The Prince of Wales's Own Regiment of Yorkshire, crosses a No. 6 Tank Bridge laid over an understressed roadbridge to allow the passage of heavy AFVs, a technique known as 'overbridging'.

69. Infantrymen dismount from an FV432 Mk 1 and an FV432 Mk 2 fitted with a 30mm Rarden turret during training at the School of Infantry at Warminster. This photograph clearly illustrates the different exhaust systems of the Mks 1 and 2, that of the Mk 1 passing over the roof and the Mk 2's being fitted along the hull side. The Mk 2 also incorporates stowage lockers on the rear hull.

70. An FV432 Mk 2/1 of the Royal Irish Rangers, mounting the 30mm Rarden turret as fitted to Fox and Scimitar, shelters beside a farm barn as it acts in the forward reconnaissance role during Exercise 'Swordthrust', October 1975. The type was conceived to provide mechanised infantry battalions with a fire support and anti-APC capability, but only 13 conversions were completed for troop trials because the FV107 Scimitar fulfils the same role.

70▶

▲71 ▼72

73▲

74▲

71. After the termination of the project, the Rarden FV432s were issued to the Berlin Field Force, where they provide an effective addition to the firepower of the garrison. With a three-man crew, the vehicle carries 99 rounds of 30mm ammunition, loaded in clips of three, that can be fired singly or in bursts at a theoretical rate of 90 rounds per minute. Here, Rarden FV432s take part in the Allied Forces Day Parade in Berlin.

72. The FV438 is a conversion of the FV432 APC to carry the Swingfire anti-tank guided weapon system. The vehicle features a fixed cupola at the rear, together with two missile launcher bins that are loaded from the inside, where a further 14 missiles are stowed. The FV438 is manned by three crew members of the

Royal Artillery and is issued on a scale of six vehicles per armoured regiment and two per mechanised infantry battalion.

73. A Swingfire missile is launched from an FV438 of the 1st Battalion The Staffordshire Regiment on the Bergen-Hohne ranges in West Germany. In action, the bin launchers are raised and the gunner tracks the target through the elevating periscopic sight, controlling the missile's flight with a joystick that sends direction commands by means of a wire trailing from the missile.

74. A Royal Engineers FV432 Mk 1 tows a Bar Mine Layer, which is loaded by Sappers inside the vehicle while under armour protection. The system sows anti-tank mines rapidly, and the Bar Mine is capable of disabling all current tanks. (Simon Dunstan)

43

▲75

75. Ranger anti-personnel mines are fired from a multi-barrel projector mounted on the roof of an FV432 Mk 2/1. The projector has 72 tubes, each containing 18 mines that are fired individually to a range of 100m in a random pattern. The Ranger is often used in conjunction with the Bar Mine Layer (as illustrated) so that the anti-personnel mines hinder the clearing of anti-tank minefields.
76. An FV434 Mk 1/1 Tracked Maintenance Carrier tows an

immobilized FV432 Mk 2 APC during an exercise in West Germany. The vehicle is operated by members of the Royal Electrical and Mechanical Engineers and has a four-man crew. Typically on 434s, the 'recy mechs' have erected a tarpaulin over the rear compartment to create a more comfortable working and sleeping area.

▼76

77. An FV107 Scimitar moves across the prairie in Canada between white tapes denoting a cleared path through a minefield.

78. An FV105 Sultan armoured command vehicle executes a sharp turn at speed. (Simon Dunstan)

79. Wearing its prominent red crosses, an FV104 Samaritan armoured ambulance moves forward during training at Bovington. (Simon Dunstan)

80. The FV721 Combat Vehicle Reconnaissance (Wheeled) Fox armoured car is used by UK-based armoured reconnaissance regiments. (Simon Dunstan)

81. A Chieftain Mk 5 Armoured Recovery Vehicle pulls a disabled tank to safety by means of its front-mounted winch. (Simon Dunstan)

82. The Royal Electrical and Mechanical Engineers crew of a Centurion ARV Mk 2 recover a stranded vehicle on Bordon Heath. (Simon Dunstan)

79▶

▼80

▲83 ▼84

85▲

83. A Centurion BARV (Beach Armoured Recovery Vehicle) moves through the shallows at Fording Trials Branch (REME), Instow, Devon. (Simon Dunstan)

84. A Tracked Rapier and its M548 Support Vehicle moves forward under the covering guns of a Scorpion and a Scimitar. (Simon Dunstan)

85. The principal role of the FV434 is to change major assemblies such as engines and gearboxes in the field. Here an FV434 Mk 1/1 lowers a new powerpack into an FV432 by means of its HIAB hydraulic crane. The first 16 FV434 vehicles built (00ED74–00ED89) had no provision for a heater in the crew compartment and were designated Mk 1; all subsequent vehicles have provision for a heater and are designated FV434 Mk 1/1.

86. The latest APC to enter service with the British Army is the GKN Sankey AT105 Saxon. Designed primarily for the internal security role, it is of simple construction and incorporates conventional automotive components, which makes it reliable, easy to maintain and, by today's standards for AFVs, inexpensive. The Saxon is armed with a twin GPMG turret and is equipped with vision blocks and firing ports for the eight infantrymen carried inside.

◀86

88

87. (Previous spread) One of the most important AFVs in mechanised warfare is an armoured recovery vehicle to retrieve disabled tanks on the battlefield, even under hostile fire. For ease of training and logistics the ARV is usually produced around the chassis of the current battle tank. The FV4204 ARV is based on the Chieftain Mk 5 and is deployed at combat·team and battle-group level as part of the equipment of an armoured workshop.
88. A Chieftain Mk 5 ARV recovers a bogged tank by means of its front-mounted winch, its dozer blade lowered for stability. The

main winch has a pulling capacity of 30,000kg but with block and tackle this can be increased to 90,000kg, which is sufficient to recover the heaviest of tanks. (Simon Dunstan)
89. In a cloud of dust, a Chieftain Mk 5 ARV speeds to another assignment. With the introduction of the Challenger MBT into service, the Chieftain ARV fleet is being modified by fitting an Atlas AK 6000M crane and a cradle to accommodate a complete Challenger powerpack. In this guise, it is designated Chieftain Mk 7 Armoured Recovery and Repair Vehicle (ARRV).

▼**89**

90. During the course of the Chieftain ARRV modification programme, the redoubtable Centurion ARV Mk 2 has been returned to the front line. This simple and rugged vehicle has given many years of unfailing service and it retains many advocates who prefer it to its sophisticated successor. This particular Centurion ARV Mk 2 serves with the 32nd Armoured Engineer Regiment at Munsterlager in West Germany.

91. Heir to the great traditions of 79th Armoured Division is the 32nd Armoured Engineer Regiment, whose task is to maintain the mobility of friendly forces and to deny mobility to the enemy. To this end, the Sappers are equipped with a range of specialized vehicles of which the Centurion Mk 5 AVRE (Armoured Vehicle Royal Engineers) is the general workhorse.

92. The Centurion AVRE undertakes numerous tasks on the battlefield, including the digging of anti-tank ditches or tank scrapes with its dozer blade (a tank can be dug-in to turret level in under five minutes). Conversely, it can fill ditches, and it can span gaps with a fascine made of plastic pipes as illustrated here. Its 165mm demolition gun, firing a 64lb HESH shell, can destroy hard targets such as concrete buildings and bridges.

▼92

93. The Centurion AVRE has been adapted to carry a mine plough which uproots and deflects anti-tank mines over the widt of each track. The AVRE also acts as a towing vehicle for Giant Viper mine-clearing equipment. This device is carried in a specia trailer and comprises 1½ tons of plastic explosives in a 750ft long hose that is rocket-propelled across a minefield. When fired, the mines are detonated by sympathetic explosion, forming a safe pa of up to 24ft wide; any remaining mines are cleared by the ploug

▲94 ▼95

94. Another specialized vehicle employed by the Armoured Engineers is the Chieftain Bridgelayer, or FV4205 Armoured Vehicle Launched Bridge (AVLB). The AVLB is adapted from the standard Chieftain Mk 5 and carries either of two bridges; the larger, No. 8 Tank Bridge is of the scissors type and can span a gap of 80ft. The complete launching sequence takes under five minutes.

95. Displaying the layout of its launching assembly, a Chieftain Bridgelayer crosses the AVLB that it has just positioned, during an exercise in West Germany. The bridge can be retrieved in approximately ten minutes and from either end – a significant tactical advantage in an advance of armoured units.

96. Using the smaller No. 9 Tank Bridge as a platform, a Chieftain Bridgelayer launches its No. 8 bridge across the River Leine near Hollenstadt in West Germany. By using this 'double bridging' method, the total bridging distance is greatly increased. The bridge is laid by means of rams powered by a hydraulic pump located in the hull and driven by a power take-off from the main engine.

96▶

▲97

▲98

97. The Royal Engineers also employ the FV180 Combat Engineer Tractor (CET), which was designed from the outset to fulfil the numerous tasks of the armoured combat engineers. The vehicle is fully amphibious, being propelled in water by two Dowty water jets. Constructed of aluminium, it has a large earth-moving bucket for digging tank scrapes or gun pits, clearing or creating obstacles, preparing river crossing sights and so forth. This CET is towing a Giant Viper mine clearing equipment trailer.

98. When confronted with an unscaleable obstacle or river bank, the CET can fire a rocket-propelled ground anchor and pull itself out of difficulty by means of a two-speed winch which can also be used for towing other vehicles. Both crewmen have driving controls, and the CET can be driven forwards or backwards by either of them.

99. An FV180 Combat Engineer Tractor digs a hull-down fire position for a Chieftain MBT. (Simon Dunstan)

100. By means of a jib crane mounted in the earth bucket, a CET lays Class 60 Trackway over a crossing site during an exercise in West Germany. The CET entered service in 1978, and 141 have been built for the British Army. During the Falklands War one vehicle was landed at San Carlos where, however, it achieved only limited success.

99▼

100▼

▲101

101. The Centurion Beach Armoured Recovery Vehicle (BARV) is a specialized vehicle for use in amphibious landings; it can pull disabled vehicles from deep water to the shore and also push stranded landing craft from the beaches. BARVs are manned by Royal Marines and serve aboard the Royal Naval Amphibious Assault Ships *Fearless* and *Intrepid*. Two BARVs saw action during the Falklands War.

102. Originally designed for the Imperial Iranian Army, Tracked Rapier is based on the M548 tracked cargo carrier of the M113 APC family. It entered service with the British Army in 1983, and 62 units are on order. Three Light Air Defence regiments are to be equipped with both Tracked and Towed Rapiers; a regiment will have two batteries of each system with ten firing units per battery.

103. A Tracked Rapier and its attendant support vehicle move off

▼102

during trials at Bovington; the support vehicle is a standard M5 carrying twenty missiles, with personnel and messing equipmen for the Fire Unit. The system is highly mobile, can accompany tanks and other AFVs over difficult terrain and, being amphibious, can cross inland waterways. (Simon Dunstan)

104. From coming to a halt, the RCM 748 Launcher Vehicle ca be put into action within 30 seconds. The operator controls the firing of the eight on-board missiles from inside the armoured c and in cases where the missile is launched over the cab, as illustrated, the microwave command link antenna at the rear is raised to obtain an unobstructed view. Tracked Rapier provides long overdue anti-aircraft protection to the forward battle-grou of the British Army. (British Aerospace)

103▲   104▼

▼105 ▲106

5. An Abbot 105mm Self-Propelled Gun is replenished with amunition from an Alvis Stalwart (6 × 6) High Mobility Load arrier. Based on the same chassis as the FV432 APC, the FV433 bbot was manufactured by Vickers and entered service with the ritish Army in 1965, replacing the venerable Sexton 25pdr SP of cond World War vintage.

106. A troop of Abbots is prepared for action during an exercise in West Germany. Abbot is the principal weapon of Royal Artillery close support field regiments in both BAOR and the UK; each regiment has four batteries of Abbots, with two troops of three guns in each.

107. Abbots of 16 Battery (Sandham's Company), 26 Field Regiment, Royal Artillery, unleash a fire plan on the Munsterlager ranges in West Germany. Main armament comprises the L13A1 105mm gun with a double-baffle muzzle brake and a fume extractor. The weapon has a maximum elevation of 70° and depression of 5°, whilst turret traverse is a full 360°.

108. Abbot is powered by a Rolls-Royce K60 Mk 4G multi-fuel engine through a GMC Allison TX200 automatic transmission, giving a top speed of 30mph (48km/h) to a maximum range of 240 miles (390km). The vehicle is amphibious (a flotation screen is fitted around the top of the hull) and is protected against NBC contamination.

107▶

▼108

▲109

109. For the export market, Vickers has developed a simplified version of the FV433 known as the Value Engineered Abbot, although, in order to reduce procurement costs, this model lacks such refinements as the flotation screen, NBC pack and multi-fuel engine capability. It is in service with the Indian Army, and the British Army purchased four of them for use at the Suffield training area in Canada. The example seen here is operated by th 1st Cheshire Battle Group.

110. An M107 175mm Self-Propelled Gun of 32 Heavy Regiment, Royal Artillery, moves across rough terrain on a rang in West Germany. The M107 entered service with the British Army in 1965 and provides general artillery support in the field.

▼110

66

1. Concealed beneath camouflage netting in a German orchard, M107 awaits its next fire mission. The weapon is served by a -man crew, five of whom travel on the vehicle and the mainder on a supporting cargo carrier with the ammunition. he M107 is a fine weapon system, as proven in Vietnam, in the ctober War of 1973 and in the Lebanon.

112. Members of 32 Heavy Regiment, Royal Artillery, fire their M107 SPGs on the ranges in West Germany. The 175mm gun fires only an HE projectile to a maximum range of 32,700m, giving the longest reach of any tube artillery weapon in NATO; for this reason the M107 is employed far behind the front lines, and no armour protection is provided for the vehicle.

113. The standard equipment of the Royal Artillery's medium self-propelled batteries is the M109 155mm Self-Propelled Howitzer, as seen here with 39 Medium Regiment, RA, during training at Munsterlager in West Germany. The M109 entered service with the British Army in 1965.

114. The main armament of the M109 is the 155mm howitzer M126, with its distinctive fume extractor behind the muzzle brake. The weapon fires an extensive range of ammunition to a maximum range of 14,600m. Weighing 23 tons, the M109 has a crew of eight and, despite its bulk, has an amphibious capability.

115. M109 Self-Propelled Howitzers of 176 (Abu Klea) Battery, 39 Medium Regiment, Royal Artillery, undertake a fire plan from camouflaged positions on the Munsterlager ranges in West Germany.

116. From 1978, the M109s of the British Army were fitted with longer M185 barrels, changing the vehicle designation to M109A1. This M109A1 of 45 Field Regiment, RA, illustrates the greater length of the weapon, which increases ranges to over 18,000m.

▲113 ▼114

▼115

116▶

▲117 ▼118

119▲

117. A 155mm projectile emerges from the barrel of an M109A1 of 45 Field Regiment, RA, during gunnery training. All M109s of the British Army have been modified to A1 standard, and a further quantity of new-build vehicles, designated M109A2, have been procured. The M109A2 incorporates a number of further improvements and, in time, the M109A1s will be modified to the same configuration (becoming the M109A3).

118. Based on the same chassis as the M107, the M110 8in Self-Propelled Howitzer forms the heavy component of the Royal Artillery's conventional weapons; one battery is attached to each armoured division within BAOR. Here an M110 of 'H' Battery (Ramsay's Troop), 39 Regiment, RA, undergoes training at Lagen Trauen in West Germany.

119. Weighing 28 tons and with an eleven-man crew, the M110 fires both high-explosive and nuclear shells to a range of 14 miles. Here an M110 8in Self-Propelled Howitzer of 45 Field Regiment, Royal Artillery, fires as its crew shelters from the muzzle blast. The M110 fleet is currently being modified to A2 standard, a longer gun barrel giving an increased range capability.

120. Slung beneath the crane of an M688 Loader-Transporter (LT), a warhead is attached to a Lance missile aboard an M752 Self-Propelled Launcher (SPL). Lance is the heaviest weapon in the Royal Artillery inventory, capable of delivering a tactical nuclear device to a range of 120km.

120▼

▲121 ▼122

121. A Lance missile of 50 Missile Regiment, Royal Artillery, is prepared for firing from the depths of a West German forest. No. 50 Missile Regiment comprises four batteries, each of which has three launcher sections of SPLs supported by two sections equipped with LTs.

122. The MGM-52C surface-to-surface guided missile of the Lance weapon system is launched during firing trials in the Hebrides.